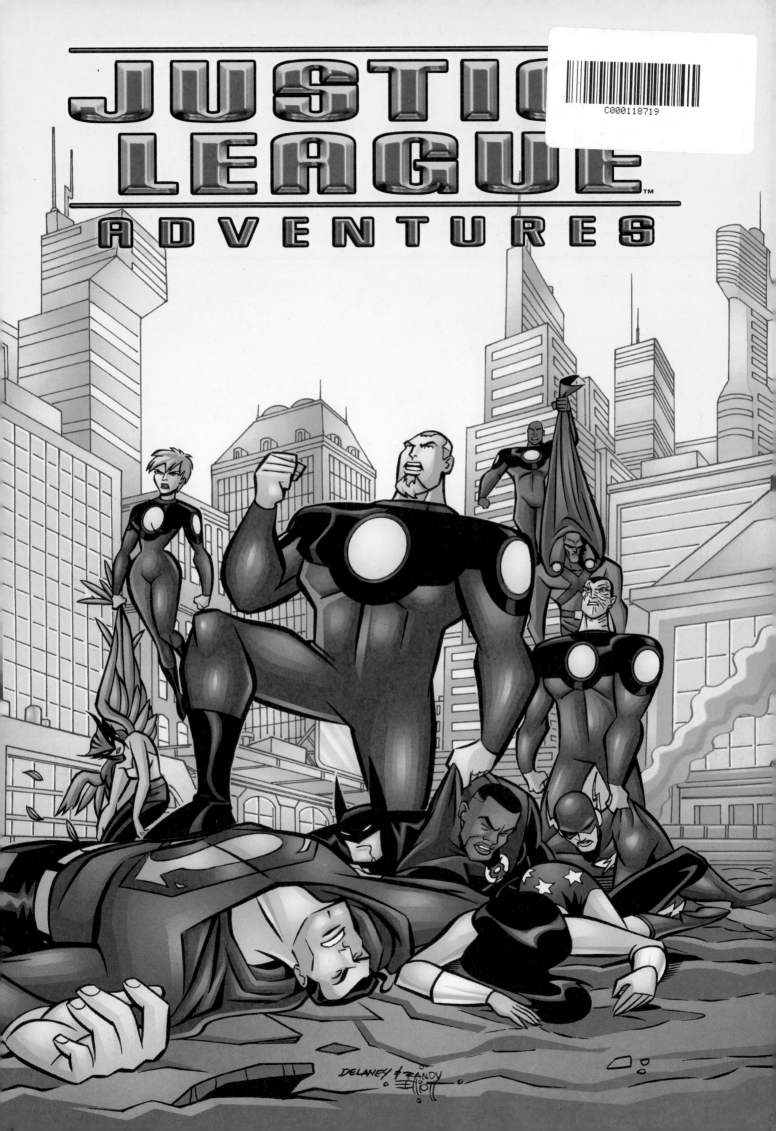

C000118719

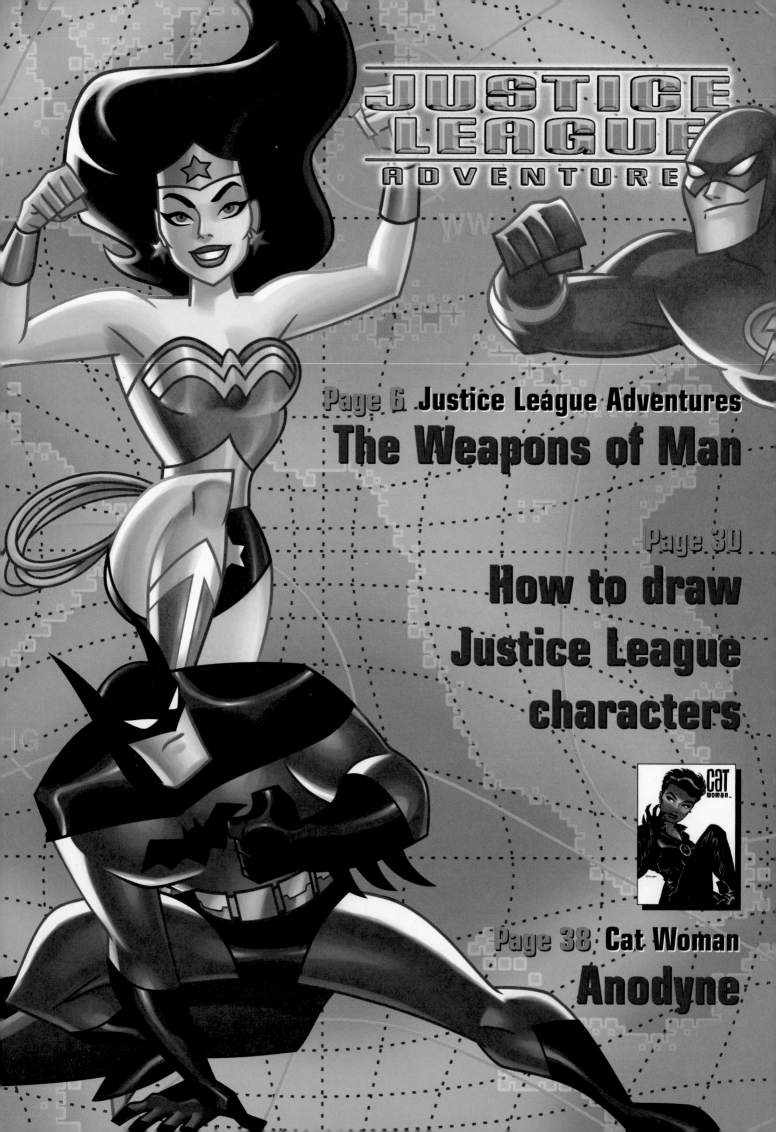

JUSTICE LEAGUE ADVENTURE

JUSTICE LEAGUE ADVENTURES

Pedigree®

Published 2004 by Pedigree Books Limited
Beech Hill House, Walnut Gardens,
Exeter, Devon, EX4 4DH.
E-mail books@pedigreegroup.co.uk

Copyright © 2004 DC Comics.
All Rights Reserved.

Justice League and all characters and
related elements appearing in this book
are trademarks of DC Comics

£6.99

JUSTICE LEAGUE ADVENTURES
OBEY ME... OR YOUR TEAMMATES DIE!
MANLEY
THE RETURN OF... ARESIA!

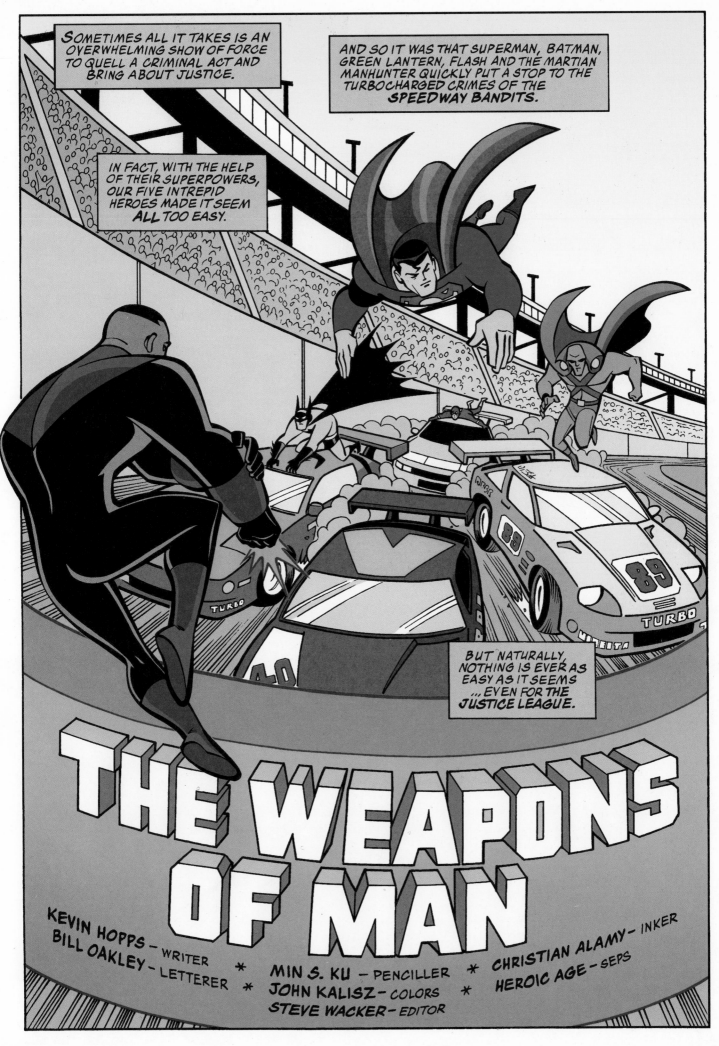

THE WEAPONS OF MAN

KEVIN HOPPS — WRITER
BILL OAKLEY — LETTERER * MIN S. KU — PENCILLER * CHRISTIAN ALAMY — INKER
JOHN KALISZ — COLORS * HEROIC AGE — SEPS
STEVE WACKER — EDITOR

MOMENTS LATER...

LOOKS LIKE WE MISSED ONE.

LOOKS ARE DECEIVING. BE RIGHT BACK.

SKREECH!

PERFECT. CATCH ME...

...IF YOU CAN.

SKREECH!

YOU KNOW, JUST ONCE I'D LIKE TO CHASE SOMEONE WITHOUT THAT WHOLE "DO I GO AFTER THE BAD GUY OR DO I RESCUE THE INNOCENT BYSTANDERS" DILEMMA.

EEEEECCH!

HMM... TRENDY CAFE. NICE.

'COURSE I'M A FAST FOOD GUY MYSELF.

WOOOOOSH

SKREECH!

BAM!

WRRRRR

SKLING

SKLING

SKLING

WELL, WELL, OUR OLD PAL ARESIA.

BBS
D'YEAR

SKRZZZ

Heh. THAT OUGHTA SLOW YOU DOWN!

CAMPOS A

SKEEB

G-FORCE T/A

MEANWHILE, BACK AT THE SPEEDWAY...

GOOD THING WE WERE IN THE NEIGHBORHOOD.

SPEEDING OFF WITH THE GRAND PRIX PRIZE MONEY BEFORE THE RACE...

THAT'S NOT VERY FAIR, NOW...

...IS IT, LADIES?

WHAT DO YOU KNOW ABOUT FAIR? YOU'RE ALL MEN.

YOU LIVE YOUR WHOLE LIVES DISCRIMINATING AGAINST WOMEN.

AND FOR THAT...

WHAT'S SHE...

GET BACK!

EEEEEE

EEEEE

...FOR THAT YOU SUFFER.

12

CLAIMING RESPONSIBILITY FOR MASTERMINDING TODAY'S STARTLING EVENT IS A WOMAN KNOWN ONLY AS...

...ARESIA.

LIVE

WOMEN OF THE WORLD, FEAR NOT. SOON, ALL MEN WILL OBEY MY EVERY WORD.

BUT HOW DID...?

AND IT'S ALL POSSIBLE THANKS TO MY REVOLUTIONARY SONIC EQUALIZER.

SOUNDS LIKE AN INFOMERCIAL.

SOUNDS LIKE TROUBLE.

AT CLOSE RANGE, THE EQUALIZER'S HIGH-PITCHED, HYPNOTIC FREQUENCY CAN BE HEARD ONLY BY MEN.

EEEEEEEEE

MAKING THE WORLD A BETTER PLACE FOR ALL...

OR, AT LEAST, FOR ME!

OKAY, I'VE SEEN ENOUGH.

ARESIA. I REMEMBER HER... THE *MAN HATER*.

AT *LEAST* YOU CAN UNDERSTAND HER MOTIVATION.

"TORN FROM HER HOMELAND DURING A *BARBARIC* CIVIL WAR BROUGHT ON BY *MEN*.

"HER REFUGEE SHIP PLUNDERED AND SUNK BY *MALE PIRATES*."

"FORTUNATELY, SHE WASHED ASHORE ON MY HOME, THEMYSCIRA.

"FREE FROM MAN'S INJUSTICES, SHE TRAINED AND WAS MAGICALLY ENDOWED WITH *AMAZON STRENGTH* BY MY SISTERS.

"EVERY DAY SHE GREW STRONGER.

"AS DID HER *ANGER* AND *HATRED* TOWARDS MAN.

"THAT'S WHY WE HAVE TO *FIND* ARESIA AND FIND HER FAST... BEFORE SHE DESTROYS MANKIND."

CRACK

WELL, WHAT ARE WE WAITING FOR? IF ARESIA IS IN THERE, LET'S BLAST ON DOWN AND GRAB HER!

AND LET ARESIA DO TO *YOU* WHAT SHE'S DONE TO THE *OTHER MEN?*

OKAY... BUT I'M NOT GONNA JUST STAND AROUND.

I LET THE GUYS DOWN WHEN THAT *SPEEDING BEAUTY* SLIPPED THROUGH MY FINGERS.

IT *WON'T* HAPPEN AGAIN ...BUT I NEED A PLAN.

AND I THINK I HAVE AN IDEA.

FINE. JUST *STOP PACING,* YOU'RE MAKING ME DIZZY.

AND MAKE HASTE. THERE IS NOT MUCH TIME.

"OUR BOYS ARE ON THE *MOVE.*"

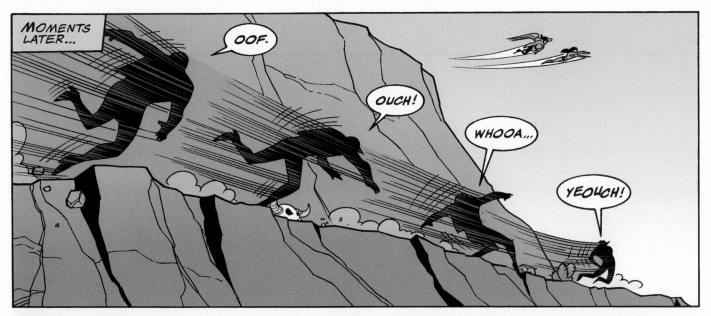

ACROSS THE SEVEN CONTINENTS, THROUGH-OUT TIME, MAN HAS AMASSED HIS WEAPONS OF WAR.

BUT *NOW*, MAN'S MIGHT AND EGO WILL BE HIS *DOWNFALL*.

HAWKGIRL... DON'T WANT TO *BRAG*, BUT...

...SNEAKING INTO ARESIA'S HIDEOUT? *NO* PROB--

HEY!

Uh... MAKE THAT... *SMALL* PROBLEM.

RATATAT ATA TATATA

TERRIFIC. MY HAIR'S A MESS, MY LIPSTICK'S SMEARED, AND *NOW*, I'VE GOT A MAJOR RUN IN MY STOCKINGS!

WELCOME TO A WOMAN'S WORLD.

SO GLAD YOU COULD *JOIN* US.

EEEEEEE

THE PACIFIC OCEAN.

I THOUGHT SUPERMAN AND GREEN LANTERN WERE ON OUR SIDE.

THINK AGAIN.

SZZZZZ

SUPERMAN! GREEN LANTERN!

STOP!

I'M SORRY...

DO WE KNOW YOU?

19

I'M PRINCESS DIANA. **WONDER WOMAN?** I WORK WITH YOU.

RIGHT. WONDER WOMAN. OF COURSE, I REMEMBER NOW.

THANK ATHENA.

ARESIA **WARNED** US THAT YOU MIGHT TRY TO INTERFERE.

WHAAM!

SUPERMAN, **WAIT!** WE'RE ON THE SAME TEAM. THE **JUSTICE LEAGUE!**

THEN HELP US CAPTURE THIS AIRCRAFT CARRIER.

NO. LISTEN TO ME. ARESIA. SHE HAS YOU UNDER HER POWER. SHE'S **FORCING YOU** TO OBEY HER.

WRONG! WE OBEY ARESIA BECAUSE...

...BECAUSE...

...BECAUSE SHE **TOLD** US TO!

THOOOM!

THE JUNGLES OF CHINA.

FWOOSH

UNH!

FWOOM!

HELLO, BOYS. REMEMBER ME? HAWKGIRL?

LATER...

I STILL DON'T REMEMBER A THING.

BUT I'M GRATEFUL THAT WONDER WOMAN, HAWKGIRL AND LADY FLASH WERE THERE TO HELP SAVE OUR SKINS.

WE SHOULD ALSO BE GRATEFUL THAT THE EQUALIZER'S HYPNO POWERS WERE ONLY TEMPORARY.

AND THAT WE DESTROYED THE DEVICE.

YEAH, WELL, AS GRATEFUL AS WE ALL ARE, ARESIA'S GOTTA BE THE MOST GRATEFUL.

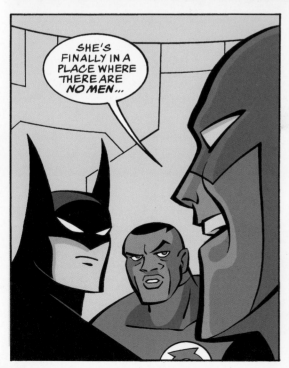

SHE'S FINALLY IN A PLACE WHERE THERE ARE NO MEN...

"...AN ALL WOMEN'S PRISON."

THE END

SUPERMAN

Sent to Earth from the exploding planet Krypton, Superman was raised by Jonathan and Martha Kent, who named him Clark. After traveling for many years, Clark Kent moved to Metropolis, where he became a reporter at the *Daily Planet* newspaper. His role as a journalist has alerted him to thousands of emergencies over the years. And as Superman he has fought tirelessly to defend Earth and protect all people.

Learn to draw your favourite super heros by following our simple step-by-step guides.

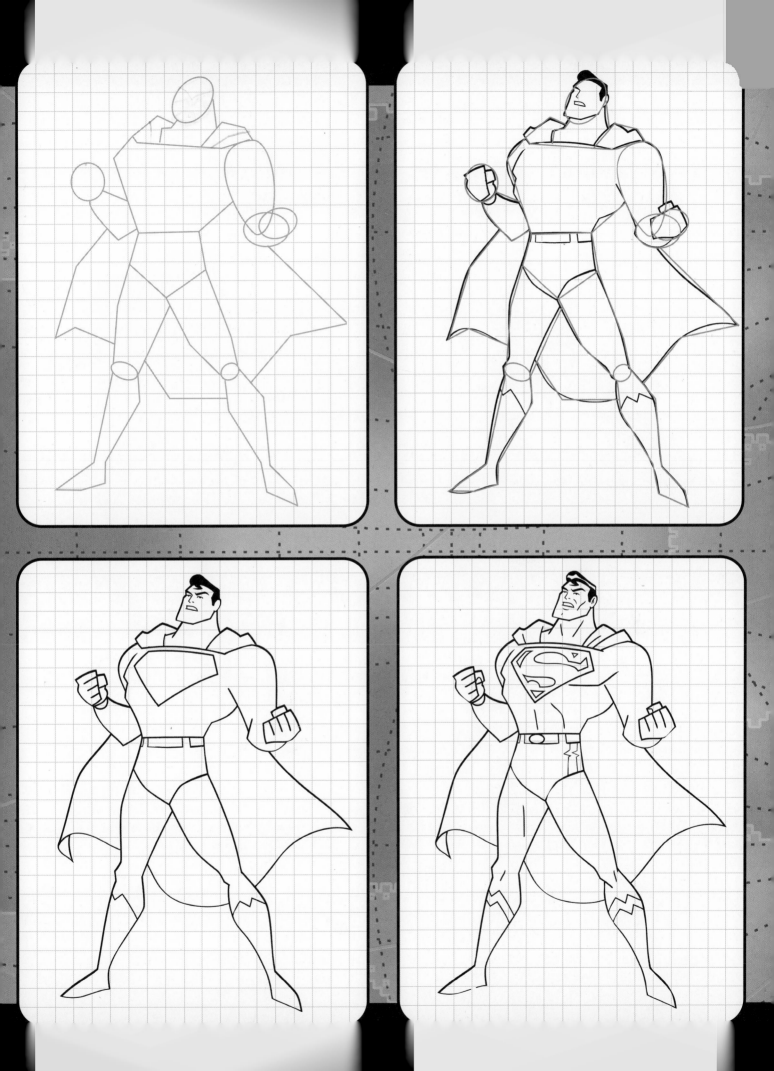

BATMAN

Bruce Wayne saw his parents killed in front of him and, from that day forward, he dedicated his life to eradicating crime. Trained to the peak of physical and mental perfection, Batman stands guard over Gotham City and, when duty calls, the World's Greatest Detective joins forces with the heroes of the Justice League to fight for justice throughout the world.

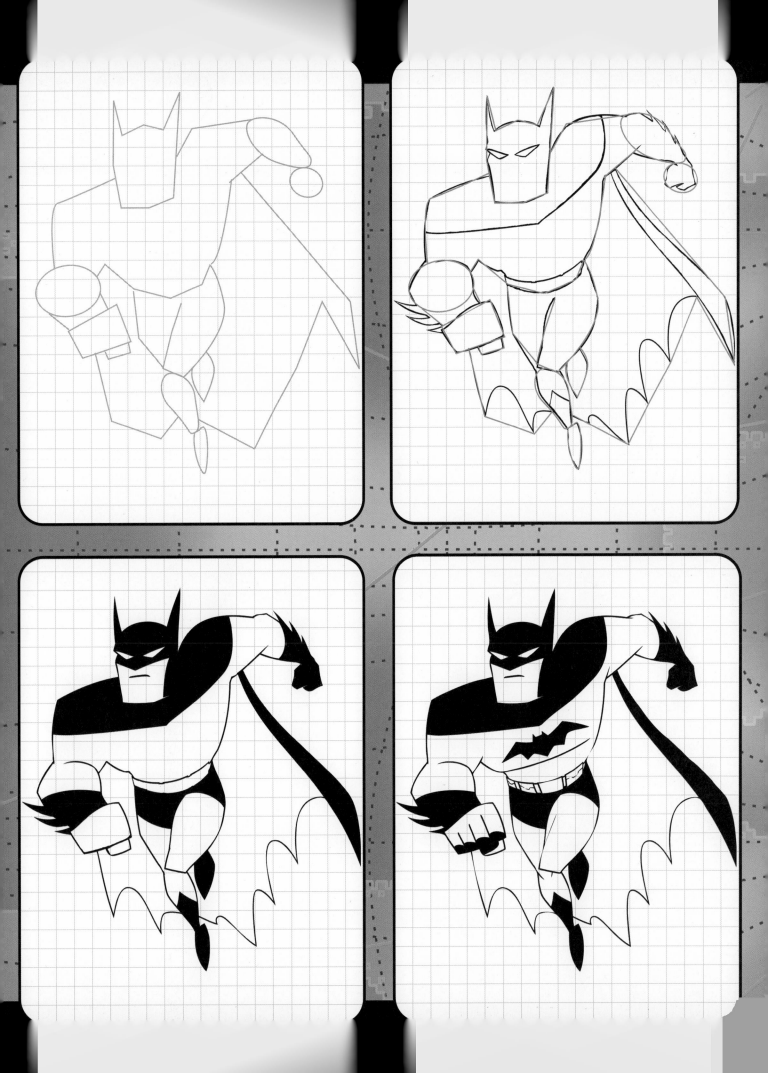

WONDER WOMAN

Daughter of the Amazon queen Hippolyta, Princess Diana of Themyscira was blessed at birth with amazing strength and wisdom. As Wonder Woman, Diana left her Amazon sisters to fight evil in our world. Wonder Woman is the ultimate Amazon warrior and a force to be reckoned with even in the formidable ranks of the Justice League.

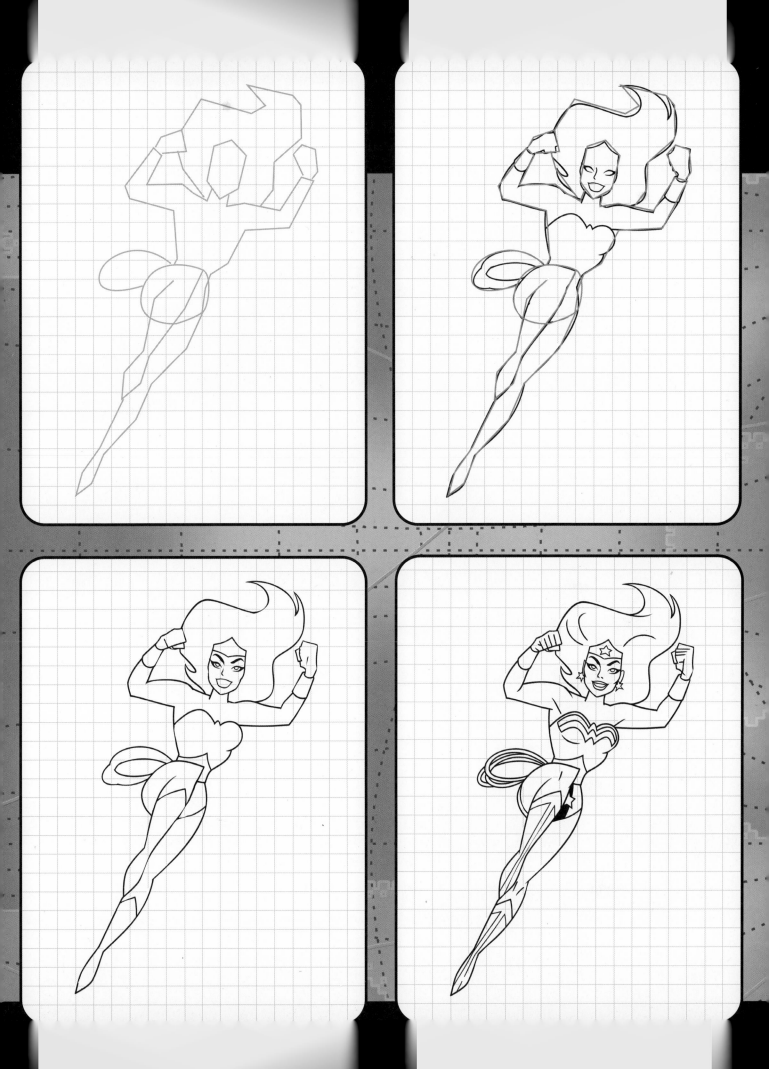

THE FLASH

Young, brash, and impulsive, Wally West gained the power of superspeed during a freak electrochemical accident. Now the Flash is the Fastest Man Alive, capable of speeds approaching that of light. But even if he often acts before he thinks, the Flash is the first one to race into the fight . . . and the superspeeding winner in many a race against doom with the Justice League.

OLD GOTHAM, THE EAST END, FAR TOO LATE...

LOOKIN' FOR A PARTY?

YEAH, I AM, ACTUALLY...

... CAN YOU HELP ME OUT WITH THAT?

OH, I GUESS WE COULD WORK SOMETHIN' OUT...

GET IN.

UNT UH... SORRY, I DON'T DO CAR DATES WITH GUYS I DON'T KNOW.

OKAY, MY NAME'S BRIAN.

GLAD TO MEET YOU...?

I'M LISA.

I've been having trouble sleeping...
... And my dreams... well, they certainly aren't helping any.
I can't remember much of them-- but I wake up feeling like my whole life is slipping right through my fingers.
anodyne

And I have these little shards of images that, sort of... echo in my head.

Like everything I've ever been is struggling inside me...

... trying to find some place to fit themselves.

To find some truth.

AND, FOR SOME REASON, I KEEP THINKING ABOUT MY SISTER...

... BUT I DON'T REALLY KNOW WHY.

I MEAN, I HAVEN'T SEEN HER IN... GOD, YEARS.

Mmmhmm... WELL, THERE'S NO NEED FOR MY PSYCHOANALYSIS.

SOUNDS LIKE YOU'RE DOING A DECENT JOB YOUR-SELF, SELINA...

... REEVALUATE THINGS, JUST AS YOU'D PLANNED. YOU'VE GIVEN YOURSELF A BREAK FROM YOUR ROUTINE...

... NOW JUST GIVE YOURSELF A BREAK.

THANKS, DR. THOMPKINS. FOR SEEING ME SO LATE...

... AND FOR LISTENING.

IT'S NO TROUBLE, REALLY. WHY ELSE WOULD HE HAVE SENT YOU TO ME?

AND PLEASE, CALL ME LESLIE.

WELL... GOOD NIGHT THEN, LESLIE.

GOT WHAT'CHU NEED...

KIND BUDS... GOT THE KIND BUDS...

AIN'T'CHU HEARIN' ME, GIRL? SAID I GOTS WHAT'CHU NEED.

I SINCERELY DOUBT IT.

BWAHAHA!

MAN, GIRL DISSED YOU! AHA!

45

Welcome home, Selina Kyle...

Is this where you belong?

But even if it's not, where else were you going to go?

As far as most of the world is concerned, Selina Kyle is dead... So it wasn't like you could just move back into your Park Row apartment.

But this place, no one knows about this place. Not anymore. Well, maybe _he_ knows.

It's hard to say what he knows for sure.

But you hadn't even thought of this place in years. Amazing that it was still here, after all this time, and the changes that Gotham has been through.

But somehow you knew it would be, because you bought this place back in the early days to be a sanctuary...

A safe house for your friends... Holly, Monique, Darla... A secret home away from the street and the life.

Of course, all of them are long gone now, and who would have ever imagined it would be you who would need this sanctuary?

Not to hide, of course... but to slow down, take a look at your life, and the mess you've made of it.

You were a different person then. That Selina took care of people...

And how fitting that you'd have to come back to these streets, where it all began.

... and had been for as long as she could remember...

That had been one of the reasons for the mask, initially. To help provide.

That and the excitement... the adventure. Don't kid yourself that they weren't a big part of it, too.

But when did they take over?

When did you stop helping your sister, your friends, and just start helping yourself?

And when did you climb the social ladder and lose those friends entirely?

SO, THEN... WHO *ARE* YOU, SELINA KYLE?

47

Hardly any sleep last night, either.

Maybe what I need is some exercise.

My mind is probably just spinning in circles because I'm not in constant motion.

So, maybe if I work myself to exhaustion, that'll do the trick.

TWAP!

THE GOTHAM GAZETTE

SECOND BODY FOUND IN ONE WEEK

POLICE HAVE NO COMMENT ON MURDER

Anything to just shut my brain off for a few hours.

And if pushing my muscles until they tear doesn't do it...

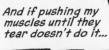

... maybe, this sunset will...

There's nothing quite like the universe to make your problems feel small...

... if only for a moment or two.

Of course, when night falls there's always something to help you lose perspective...

RATATATTA ATT

SKREECH

Him. Of course.

BAM

BRA TA TATTA TAT TAT

Gotham's own guardian angel.

In his black and white world...

KRASH

BOOM

... with his brightly-colored adversaries.

WHEN IS IT *TIME*... TO ACT LIKE A *BANANA*...?

WHEN YOU NEED... TO *SPLIT*... HEH HEH HEH...

Such a joke...

Is this my world, too?

With the boy scout...

...and the obsessive-compulsive?

MOVE, DAMN YOU! MOVE!

The violence sure feels like my world.

Without him, I wouldn't have become who I am.

And I owe him so much...

ALL OF YOU! JUST *STAY* CALM!

NOBODY PANIC, JUST MOVE *ONE* STEP AT A *TIME!*

But we've been at odds from the start. Because-- No!

NO!

At odds from the start...

... Because my world is all just shades of grey, Batman.

That's why you'll never really understand me.

It's about good people being forced into bad situations.

That's my territory...

In between right and wrong.

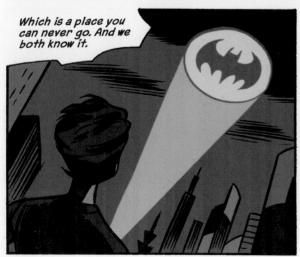

Which is a place you can never go. And we both know it.

Just like I know I'll finally sleep tonight.

mrrrowr? mrrrowr?

mrrrowr?

WHAT DO YOU WANT, *Hmmm?* DIDN'T I PUT OUT ENOUGH *FOOD*, LITTLE FLUFFY GUY?

THEN GO *EAT*, OKAY? I'VE GOT SOME STUFF TO *DO* HERE!

mrrroarrr! mrrrrr!

Dr. Thompkins... Leslie... was right. The mask is part of who I am now.

But it's also part of the problem, too...

... because it became a person all on its own.

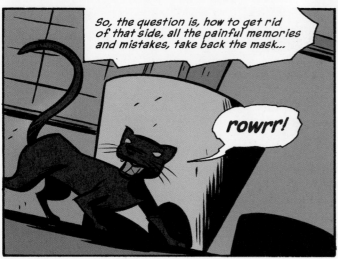

So, the question is, how to get rid of that side, all the painful memories and mistakes, take back the mask...

rowrr!

... and still be able to sleep at night. Still be able to live with myself.

I'm not sure if I can do all that, really...

... but I think I know how to try...

SURPLUS

GOV. CODE # 173
PART # H 155 AA

We can skip the tail for now...

And figure out what else to skip as time goes on.

It feels good to be a part of it all again.

The city lights...

The night...

Maybe it feels right again, for the first time in a long time.

SO, WAS THAT *YOU* THE OTHER DAY?

COULDN'T LET HIM *SHOOT* YOU, COULD I?

I'D HAVE SURVIVED IT.

YOU'RE WELCOME.

WHAT IS *THIS*, EXACTLY? THE *NEW YOU?*

I'M NOT *SURE* YET. WHAT DO YOU *THINK?*

IT LOOKS... *PRACTICAL.*

THAT'S WHAT I THOUGHT, TOO.

SO, DID YOU GO TO SEE DR. THOMPKINS?

YEAH, A FEW TIMES, ACTUALLY... YOU TOLD HER WHO I *WAS?*

I TRUST HER IMPLICITLY. YOUR SECRET'S *SAFE* WITH HER.

I'M *NOT* MAD.

IT'S KIND OF *NICE*, HAVING SOMEONE KNOW I'M STILL AROUND...

Maybe this will actually work. I'll have to give it time.

But the mask felt good again... It felt like me.

Whoever *that* is --

CHK
CHK
CLK

CHK
CHK

CHK

-- WHAT THE HELL?

SOMEONE TRYING TO PICK MY LOCK?

CHK
CLK

AHH! WAIT!

CAT
woman™

61